PRICE
50p

# This Book Belongs To

Mark        Wilson

3th      Bannoch court

Allon

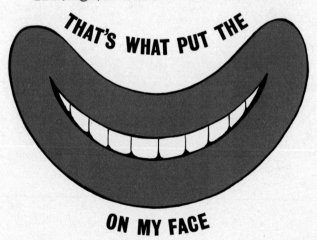

THAT'S WHAT PUT THE

ON MY FACE

# THE TOPPER BOOK

Printed and Published by D. C. THOMSON & Co., Ltd.,
12 Fetter Lane, Fleet Street, London E. C. 4.

# What a fate—when he puts on weight!

# BERYL THE PERIL

# She wins a cup—and shows Dad up!

## THE TOPPER TWINS

IF WE REMOVE THE WINDOW, MAYBE HE WON'T NOTICE!

THERE! HE'LL NEVER KNOW THE DIFFERENCE!

? SPLASH

# SHE'S ONE OF THE BEST —
# NANCY

I WONDER WHO'S AT THE POOL TODAY?

CITY SWIMMING POOL

THERE'S LITTLE TOMMY.

CITY SWIMMING POOL

HELLO, TOMMY.

HI!

?

WHAT ARE YOU DOING, TOMMY?

I DROPPED MY 5p POCKET MONEY IN THE POOL, SO I'M DRAINING IT!

# UNCLE BOB

## WITH THE ZOO-KEEPING JOB

# Tom Cat v Julius Cheeser in—
# CAT AND MOUSE GAME
## IT'S GREAT FUN!

Mid-air shocks—from a flying fox!

# BIG FAT BOKO

"My crystal-ballpoint pen. Haven't seen it for ages!"

"Try it out, master. See if it still works."

**I**N his room at Bolonia Castle, Big Fat Boko —Wonderland's hungriest wizard, had been doing a spot of tidying-up. Helped by Koko, his pet crow, the royal wizard had managed to make the place look fairly spick and span. Then, while sorting out the contents of a box of odds and ends, Boko found something rather useful . . .

The crystal-ballpoint pen was a magical pen, capable of writing, completely unaided, information about the future! Boko, setting the pen on a sheet of paper, operated its starting button.

"Right, then. Let's have some helpful hints for today!"

The pen got busy writing. And what it wrote certainly m[ade] Boko sit up!

"Be watchful in ye Zoo today— One of ye beasts will get away"

You see, at Bolonia Castle there was a very special zoo, stocked with Wonderland's rarest and strangest animals. If one should escape, Boko's royal master, King Koke, would be VERY annoyed. So Boko hurried along to warn the zoo keeper.

HAPPY THE HIPPOGLUTTON

TINY THE ARMOUR-PLATED MONSTER

GOB NGOB

ELASTIC MONKEY

Keeper

"Are all your animals safely locked up, keeper? My magic tells me that one may shortly escape."

"Impossible, wizard! Every cage is secure, and I test each lock hourly."

# CAPTAIN BUNGLE

## HE LIVES IN THE JUNGLE

# When Bungle's on the trail—you KNOW he's going to fail!

HO-HO! HA-HA!

BAH! STOP THAT CHORTLING AND LOOK OUT FOR TRACKS!

SEE? WHILE YOU WERE LAUGHING YOU NEARLY MISSED THESE ANTELOPE TRACKS!

THERE'S THE ANTELOPE—COMING BACK FROM THE WATERHOLE!

WE DON'T WANT HIM TO SPOT US! YOU HIDE IN THOSE BUSHES AND I'LL HIDE OVER HERE.

I'LL BACK WELL INTO THESE BUSHES—RIGHT OUT OF SIGHT!

BUMP!

YOW!

WHAM!

HERE'S A RHINO TRACK I DIDN'T MISS, CAP'N! AND I RECKON HE DIDN'T MISS, EITHER!

# BRITAIN'S EXTRA-SPECIAL AGENTS —
# NICK KELLY
## AND HIS ASSISTANT CEDRIC

IN THE CASE OF THE
**BUZZ-BOMB GANG**

IN NICK KELLY'S OFFICE —
MY FARM WAS RAIDED LAST NIGHT AND ALL MY BEES WERE STOLEN!

OH, NO! NOT ANOTHER ONE!

THAT'S THE FIFTH CASE OF BEE-PINCHING THIS LAST FORTNIGHT! WHO'D WANT TO PINCH BEES?

SEARCH ME, MR KELLY.

THAT NIGHT, ANOTHER FARM HAS VISITORS...

OK, LOFTY! SWITCH OFF THE VACUUM. WE'VE SUCKED UP ALL THE BEES IN HERE.

SUCK!

NOW THAT WE HAVE PLENTY AMMUNITION FOR OUR BUZZ-BOMBS, WE CAN RAID A BANK TOMORROW. HEE-HEE!

NEXT DAY —
BANK
THIS IS A HOLD-UP!

?

FIRE THE BUZZ-BOMBS!

PHUT!

PHUT!

SPLOP!

SPLOP!

# Some broken glass puts Kelly on the right track!

THEN—

ANGRY BUZZING!

BUZZ!

GRR! KIDNAPPED! COOPED UP IN A PESKY TIN CAN! SLAPPED AGAINST A WALL! OOO, I AM ANGRY!

OOO! OUCH! EEK!

STING!

STING!

STING!

RIGHT, BOYS! LET'S GRAB THE MONEY WHILE THEY'RE DANCING!

WHAT'S THAT? A RAID AT PERKIN'S BANK! WE'LL BE RIGHT OVER!

...AND THESE MEN WITH GLASS DOMES OVER THEIR HEADS FIRED BEE-FILLED CYLINDERS, THEN SWITCHED OFF OUR ALARM SYSTEM AND GRABBED THE MONEY!

HMM!

LOANS

HULLO— FRAGMENTS OF GLASS!

THAT'S A PIECE OF ONE OF THEIR GLASS HELMETS. IT MUST HAVE GOT BROKEN.

HMM! THEN THERE'S A FAIR CHANCE THAT BANDIT GOT STUNG, TOO.

LOANS

HE MUST HAVE BANGED HIS HEAD AGAINST THAT SIGN. HE'S PRETTY TALL, THEN.

AT LAST WE HAVE CLUES. HEAD FOR THE UNDERWORLD, CEDRIC. WE'RE LOOKING FOR A TALL MAN WHO HAS BEEN STUNG BY BEES.

UNDERWORLD

HERE WE ARE! KEEP YOUR EYES OPEN, CEDRIC!

JEWELLE

# Ready for the buzz-bomb bandits to strike again.

# Kelly's quick-fire tart gun puts the raiders in a jam!

# There isn't any way—of getting in today!

# For laughter and fun—he's second to none!

# FIGARO

# The future looks rosy—soon he'll be cosy!

# He's very well dressed—but no one's impressed!

# THE Topper TwiNS

# SPLODGE

HE'S A GOBLIN. NO HUMAN CAN SEE HIM — EXCEPT YOU READERS!

# The fun's really hearty—when HE'S at the party!

# At last he's got food—a whole Christmas pud!

Meanwhile, on far-off Ozz, something had happened that was to have a dramatic effect on the Whizzer Twins' Earth holiday.

King Kett—chief of the Ketts, a race of dangerous Ozz criminals—had just crash-landed his personal Kett-jet on the borders of the Land of Whizz, and was being arrested by a Whizzer border patrol.

Shortly afterwards, an emergency meeting of the Kett-Klub—the criminal king's panel of advisers—was called.

We must kidnap some Very Important Person and use him as a hostage for King Kett's release.

But most VIP's in the Planetary System are closely guarded!

There must be exceptions. Let us feed our problem into the Master Kett-puter.

An excellent suggestion!

So the Master Kett-puter was fed information, and in return chattered out certain facts...

So, Sir Alan Bright-Boyd, Britain's leading research scientist, is the best target for our operation. He is at present on holiday at Faldoon Lodge in Scotland. Only two Security guards.

Soon the uncanny machines reached Faldoon Lodge, where staff, guests and security men were stopped in their tracks by the terrible paralysing beams which flashed again and again from the Kettoads' "eyes"!

They will stay 'frozen' for about twenty minutes. We must capture Sir Alan and get out of here before then!

BANG!

But nearby—

That was a gun-shot! It came from over there!

Then—

Great Ozz! Kettoads! They can't be up to any good!

DANGER
SOFT BOG
KEEP TO THE FOOTPATH

We'll stop' em! Dial XK6 on your space-pistol—the shrinker ray, that is! Aim for the hind feet when the leading Kettoad comes within range!

take the left foot. u take the right!

Both twins were on target with the XK6 rays!

The fantastic rays shrank the Kettoad's hind feet instantly to baby size . . . . .

And when the tiny feet came down on the b moment later, they sank in, and in a second machine was hopel bogged down!

Trouble! I'll swit on the pulver-eu . . .

The Kett in the second toad was out for revenge. Willie and the Whizzers fled, zig-zagging wildly to dodge the crackling thunderbolts shooting from the "eyes" of their terrible pursuer!

He's in rang now, Krik! Quick —fire at the feet before he gets us!

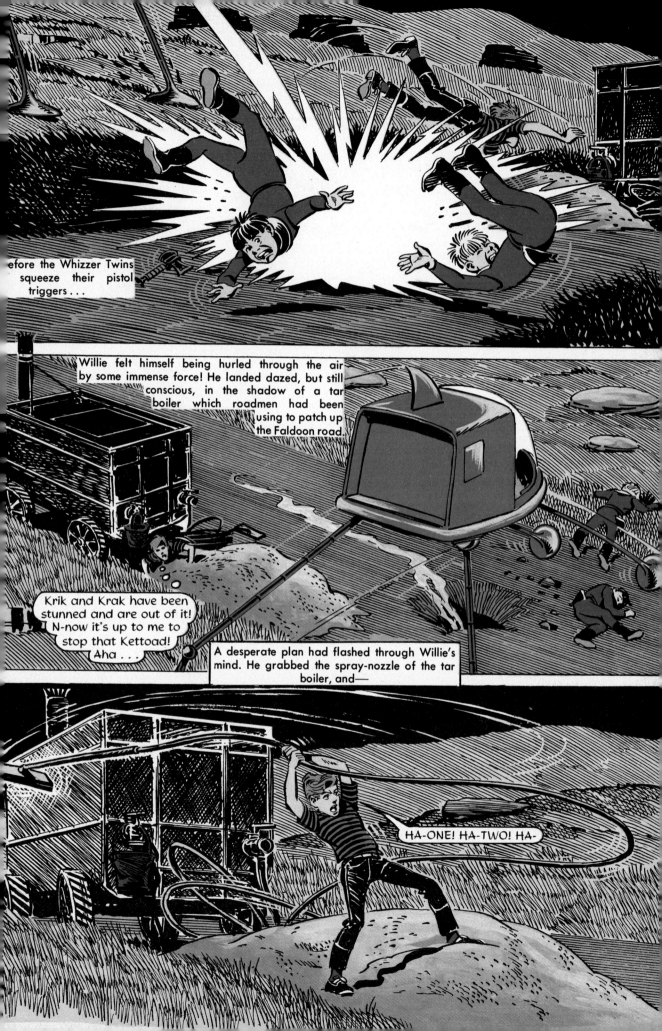

# He's off at a trot—'cos he doesn't want caught!

# Money's a sure—and certain cure!

# The boy who can peek into the future!

# SUPER SPECS

**S**PECKY SPENCER owns a pair of amazing spectacles, given to him by visitors from Outer Space. The super specs have a little knob on top and, by adjusting this knob, Specky can switch from ordinary viewing to *SEEING INTO THE FUTURE!*

AH—THERE'S THE OLD HORSE-TROUGH! WONDER IF ANY HORSES WILL DRINK HERE TODAY? I'LL SWITCH TO "FUTURE" ON MY SPECS AND FIND OUT!

HAVING SWITCHED TO "FUTURE", THIS IS WHAT SPECKY SEES.

WELL, I'M BLOWED. THAT'S P.C. DUFF, TAKING A BATH IN IT!

I SAW HIM IN THE NEXT STREET. I MUST GO AND ASK HIM WHAT TIME HE MEANS TO TAKE HIS BATH!

# BERYL the PERIL

TIME FOR HOMEWORK, BERYL... BERYL!

GET IN THERE AND GET BUSY!

AW, DAD...

HUH! THIS ALWAYS HAPPENS. BUT I'M GOING TO THINK OF SOMETHING!

NEXT DAY

I FOUND THIS OLD PICTURE OF ME, MUM. HOW ABOUT HANGING IT ON THE WALL? IT WOULD LOOK GOOD, UP HERE OPPOSITE THE T V...

ER—WELL...

LATER

THAT'S IT.

YOU'RE RIGHT— IT LOOKS FINE, BERYL!

LATER STILL...

MUM AND DAD ARE OUT —NOW, TO BORROW DAD'S TOOLS.

CRASH!

THUD!

THAT'S THE LAST OF THE MESS TIDIED UP!

# There's big trouble due—when her plan's seen through!

# Our castaway chum—has toothache, by gum!

Foxy's out of luck—hunting Moby Duck!

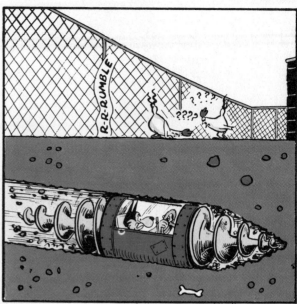

**Mickey**

THAT'S IT, POLLY. YOU'RE DOING FINE.

I THINK I'M AT OUR GATE NOW. I'LL TURN IN.

OOF! YOU'RE A LITTLE OFF COURSE, POLLY.

SEE IF YOU CAN FIND THE DOOR. YOU'RE GETTING WARM.

OH, NO. YOU'RE COLD NOW—AND GETTING COLDER.

NO, I'M GETTING WARMER. PHEW! I FEEL AS IF I'VE GOT CLOTHES ON.

HO! HO! HO!

HEY! YOU'VE DROPPED MY SHIRT IN THE COAL!

AH, WELL. NOW I KNOW I'M IN THE COAL SHED. I'LL HAVE ANOTHER GO AT FINDING THE HOUSE.

I THINK I'M GETTING CLOSE.

AH, YES. THERE'S THE DOOR KNOB.

YEOW! OOH! THAT DOES IT!

SORRY, POLLY—YOU'VE FAILED THE TEST. I CAN'T LET YOU GO TO THE CINEMA ALONE TONIGHT—

—YOU'D NEVER FIND YOUR WAY HOME IN THE DARK!

# THE WORLD'S BIGGEST DOG—

# Tiny

# He tries to impress—but it's not a success!

Though he's in disgrace—there's a grin on his face.

I SAY, I SAY— WHAT DID THE LAW OFFICER SAY TO THE PLUM PUDDING? YOU DON'T KNOW? HE SAID~"I MUST TAKE YOU INTO CUSTARDY"!

Next day, Jingo's one-pupil jesting class began. As Jingo feared, Droop was a flop...

I say, I say, what did the—er—plum pudding say—er—to the custard? I must—er—take you to the Law Officer!

No, no, Your Majesty—you STILL haven't got it right. We'll try juggling instead.

Now watch closely. This is how it's done!

TOK!

Like THIS, eh? Er—no!

Perhaps high stilt-walking might be more—er—in your line, Your Majesty? Let's give it a try, shall we?

So the sad-faced old king had a go.

Steady! Keep your balance, King Droop!

# ANOTHER LAUGH-LOADED ADVENTURE, FEATURING......

# NICK KELLY
## AND HIS ASSISTANT CEDRIC

### in the case of the Knock-Out Safe

BOUNCE!

BO-YONG-G!

ANOTHER HOLD-UP — AND THE CROOKS ARE HEADING THIS WAY?

SURELY NOT ANOTHER HOLD-UP, MR KELLY?

YES, HURRY!

THERE THEY GO — WITH THE POLICE HOT ON THEIR TAIL! STEP ON IT, CEDRIC!

WEE-WAW! WEE-WAW!

POLICE

BRRMMM!

I THINK WE'RE GAINING ON THEM!

WEE-WAW! WEE-WAW!

RRMM!

OKAY, JAKE — AT THE NEXT BEND, PRESS THE SCATTER-BUTTON FOR THE STEEL BALLS!

SUDDENLY, THOUSANDS OF BALL-BEARINGS START POURING OUT OF THE CROOKS' CAR.

WHAT—??

# The escaping villains spring a nasty surprise.

# The boss crook tells all—thanks to Kelly's fatal charm!

THERE'S BEEN NO HOLD-UP TODAY! IT'S FRIDAY 13th! THE GANG BOSS MUST BE SUPERSTITIOUS.

THEN IT COULD BE FLASH FRED! HE'S SO SUPERSTITIOUS HE WOULDN'T EVEN WALK UNDER A BLACK CAT!

LATER, FLASH FRED IS STEPPING OUT OF HIS HOUSE.

BUY A LUCKY CHARM, SIR?

YES!

THIS LUCKY HORSE-SHOE WILL BRING YOU LOTS OF GOOD LUCK, SIR!

HE FELL FOR IT, CEDRIC! FLASH FRED IS WEARING THE LUCKY CHARM.

DRIVE AROUND, JAKE! IT'S SAFER MAKING OUR PLANS IN THE CAR WHERE NOBODY CAN OVERHEAR US.

THAT LUCKY CHARM WAS A TINY RADIO TRANSMITTER! KEEP CLOSE TO THEIR CAR, CEDRIC! I CAN LISTEN TO ALL THEY SAY!

IS EVERYTHING ARRANGED FOR OUR RAID TOMORROW ON SPARKLERS THE JEWEL MERCHANTS, BERT?

YES, BOSS! BUT HOW DO WE GET THEIR SAFE OUT OF THEIR UPSTAIRS OFFICE?

EASY! WE'LL DROP IT OUT OF THE WINDOW! HEH-HEH! IT MAY EVEN BURST OPEN AND SAVE US THE JOB OF CUTTING IT OPEN!

QUICK, CEDRIC — STOP HERE! I HAVE AN IDEA MAYBE THESE PEOPLE CAN HELP US.

APEX RUBBER MANUFACTURER

LATER, KELLY DRIVES OFF WITH A MYSTERIOUS BUNDLE ON THE ROOF OF HIS CAR.

DRIVE TO SPARKLERS, THE JEWEL FIRM, CEDRIC!

# It's most unsafe to steal this safe.

# For fabulous fun—she's the famous one!
# BERYL THE PERIL

WITH A HOT-CHA-CHA... AND A HOT-CHA-CHA....!

COME IN NOW, BERYL. YOU KNOW IT'S TIME FOR YOUR MUSIC PRACTICE.

BAH! YOU SHOULD SEE THE INSTRUMENT THEY'VE GOT ME TO PLAY!

CAN'T I PLAY OUTSIDE FOR A BIT MORE, MUM, AND DO THIS LATER?

THE ONLY PLAYING YOU ARE GOING TO DO, MY GIRL, IS ON YOUR HARP!

SHE SEEMS TO KNOW ONLY TWO NOTES—AND BOTH OF THEM ARE FLAT!

TWANG!

TWING!

WELL, AT LEAST SHE'S TRYING TO PLAY SOMETHING!

# CAT AND MOUSE GAME

IF JULIUS TRIES TO GRAB THAT CHEESE HE'LL HAVE A HEAVY BOOK FALL ON HIS HEAD! HO! HO!

TOY CUPBOARD

CHEESE!

THIS TOY TRACTOR WILL SPOIL TOM'S TRAP!

TUG!

TALLY-HO!

THUD!

HO! HO! THE BOOK DIDN'T EVEN DENT THE TRACTOR!

BUT...

BAH! TOM WON'T LEAVE ME IN PEACE TO EAT THE CHEESE!

WHERE DID HE GO? I SAW HIM RUN INTO THIS ROOM!

I'LL SIT HERE TILL HE SHOWS UP.

DRAT!

I'LL UNHOOK THIS LAMP-SHADE!

TA-TA, TOM! MY BRIGHT IDEAS ALWAYS LEAVE YOU IN THE SHADE! HEE! HEE!

GRRR! LET ME OUT!

# The Mighty Midget with the amazing power hammer.

**THOR THUMB**

BRITAIN'S TINY TROUBLESHOOTER WHO WILL DEAL WITH ANY EMERGENCY, ANYWHERE.

THOR SITS IN HIS OFFICE, WAITING FOR SOMETHING TO HAPPEN...

WHAT A DULL LIFE, HAMMER. I WOULDN'T MIND A GOOD LAUGH.

THERE'S A GOOD LAUGH COMING, THOR. FOR IN A NEARBY LONDON STREET...

HEY! WHAT ARE YOU DOING?

JUST KEEPING YOU HAPPY, CONSTABLE.

A MOMENT LATER, THAT BOBBY'S HELPLESS WITH LAUGHTER.

HEE! HEE! THERE'S A THIEF! HO! HO! AND I'M LAUGHING SO MUCH I CAN'T STOP HIM. HA! HA! HA!

LOOT

NEW SCOTLAND YARD

MY LAUGH SPRAY WORKS. SOON THE WHOLE COUNTRY WILL BE HELPLESS WITH LAUGHTER—EXCEPT ME, AS LONG AS I PUFF THE SPECIAL ANTIDOTE IN MY PIPE.

IN SCOTLAND YARD...

HO! HO! HO!

WANTED REWARD

WANTED REWARD

HA! HA!

STOP THIEF!

HEE! HEE!

HO! HO! HO!

THERE—SOME MORE LAUGHING POLICEMEN. NOW TO MAKE THOR THUMB HELPLESS WITH LAUGHTER.

THOR! THERE'S SOMETHING FUNNY GOING ON! EVERYONE'S LAUGHING!

EVERYONE? HUH! I'M NOT.

AW, CHEER UP, THOR!

FZZZZZ

# When everyone starts laughing— it's not funny!

# Clouds of black smoke—put an end to the joke!